IND0112

PUFFIN BOOKS
LOOKING FOR THE RAINBOW

Born in Kasauli in 1934, Ruskin Bond grew up in Jamnagar, Dehradun, New Delhi and Simla. His first novel, *The Room on the Roof*, written when he was seventeen, received the John Llewellyn Rhys Memorial Prize in 1957. Since then he has written over five hundred short stories, essays and novellas (some included in the collections *Dust on the Mountain* and *Classic Ruskin Bond*) and more than forty books for children.

He received the Sahitya Akademi Award for English writing in India in 1993, the Padma Shri in 1999 and the Delhi government's Lifetime Achievement Award in 2012. He was awarded the Sahitya Akademi's Bal Sahitya Puraskar for his 'total contribution to children's literature' in 2013 and was honoured with the Padma Bhushan in 2014. He lives in Landour, Mussoorie, with his extended family.

Ruskin Bond

Also in Puffin by Ruskin Bond

RUSKIN BOND

LOOKING FOR THE
RAINBOW

my years
with
Daddy

Illustrations by Mihir Joglekar

PUFFIN BOOKS

PUFFIN BOOKS

USA | Canada | UK | Ireland | Australia
New Zealand | India | South Africa | China

Penguin Books is part of the Penguin Random House group of companies
whose addresses can be found at global.penguinrandomhouse.com

Published by Penguin Random House India Pvt. Ltd
7th Floor, Infinity Tower C, DLF Cyber City,
Gurgaon 122 002, Haryana, India

First published in Puffin Books by Penguin Random House India 2017

ISBN 9780143441076

Typeset in Baskerville
Book layout by Neeraj Nath
Printed at Replika Press Pvt. Ltd, India

www.penguin.co.in

Foreword

Or should I say a Backward?

Sometimes memory improves with age! It isn't all forgetfulness and muddle. As I sit here, soaking up the mellow spring sunshine, the distant past looms up before me, and I remember things that I thought I had forgotten.

Most of all I remember my father—'Daddy', as I always called him.

What is it that we want from those we love? Tenderness, mainly. And that comes but rarely in a life full of stress and strife.

Not many fathers are capable of tenderness towards their children. They are usually too busy 'earning a living for the family'—or that's the excuse! So I was lucky to have a father who gave me nearly all his spare time, who brought me books, took me for walks, shared his interests with me and held my hand in the dark.

When we are small we need someone to hold our hand in the dark.

My parents had separated, and for two years I lived with my father. Then I lost him. But they were two wonderful years, and in writing about them more than seventy years later, I find that they are still as vivid and alive with tender emotions as they were such a long time ago.

And how lucky I am to be able to remember it all.

The doors of memory open, and they are standing there—my father, my friends, my good companions. And not forgetting the jamun trees, and guava jelly for breakfast.

Ruskin Bond
Landour, Mussoorie
4 March 2017

LONG AGO IN NEW DELHI

1

An entire year without school! What more could an eight-year-old boy ask for? Not what his parents would ask for, certainly; but after serving a two-year sentence in a fun-less convent school in the hills, I was more than happy to take a long, enforced break from gloomy classrooms, smelly dormitories, an overcrowded playing field and a diet of cabbage soup and boiled meat.

That was the sort of school I'd escaped from— or rather, been plucked out of by my father in the middle of the summer term.

It was 1942, the middle of World War II, and my parents too had been at war with each other. They had, in fact, separated, and my mother was about to marry again. My father was serving in the Royal Air Force, and was living on his own in an Air Force hutment in New Delhi, working in the Codes and Cyphers section at Air Headquarters. I was particularly close to my father, and I insisted on going to live with him rather than to a new and unknown home.

My mother took me out of the hill school near her home in Dehradun and put me on the train to Delhi.

My father was on the station platform in Delhi, looking very smart in his RAF uniform. He hugged me, took me by the hand and led me to the station restaurant, where we had a healthy breakfast. Even a railway breakfast was better than the fare we had at school!

We were joined by my uncle Fred, who was then the station superintendent at the Old Delhi station. He had a bungalow nearby. But my father's quarters, or hutments as they were called, were at the other end of Delhi, on Humayun Road, where the new capital of India had been created.

We must remember that up until then, Calcutta had been the capital of British-ruled India, and Simla, the summer capital. Now the capital was New Delhi, still very new and still coming up, and Simla, of course, was much nearer.

The hutment was a bit of a surprise. It consisted of two brick-walled rooms, a kitchen and a bathroom. And it was in the middle of nowhere.

Humayun Road, in those far-off days, was simply a lane running through a scrub forest. It had been cleared in places so that these wartime hutments could come up. But there were more jackals than people in the area. And snakes too.

2

I saw my first snake that summer. It came gliding out of the thorn bushes behind the hutment and slithered gracefully across the small stretch of short grass that passed for a garden. I had no idea if it was venomous and I wasn't about to try and find out. How can you tell if a snake is venomous or not? A cobra is unmistakable because of its spreading hood, and a banded viper would stand out, but most snakes look alike to small boys.

This was a long, black snake with a flat head. It probably wasn't venomous, because it was immediately attacked by three bold hens who emerged from the bushes and flung themselves at the reptile, pecking at it and trying to lift it off the ground. Perhaps they had mistaken it for a giant worm. Or perhaps they were protecting their chicks. They reminded me of my aunts in Dehra, chasing a schoolboy out of the guava orchard.

Anyway, the snake made no attempt to retaliate, and simply disappeared into the undergrowth.

'Don't go too far from the house, Ruskin,' warned my father. 'It's still quite wild around here.'

He gave me the habit of knocking out and examining my shoes every morning. I did not realize the importance of doing this, until one day a centipede dropped out of one of my shoes.

After that I was very careful to examine them. And it's a habit that is still with me. Only the other day I found a harmless little skink (a tiny member of the lizard family) in one of

my shoes. It would have been crushed
had I put my shoe on without the
usual examination. Anyway, I
deposited the little fellow
(who reminded me of
Bill the lizard from *Alice
in Wonderland*) on to the
base of my rubber
plant, and he

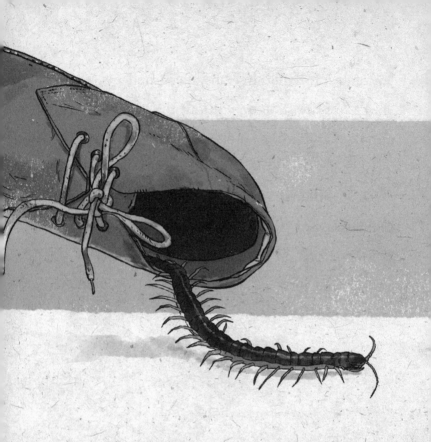

seemed quite content there. But we have no control over the vagaries of nature. The next day he fell victim to a marauding cat.

But to return to New Delhi in the summer of 1942—

It was hot, exceedingly hot, and the loo, or winds from the Rajputana desert, brought no relief. They were hot, dusty winds. Sometimes there was a dust storm, which would be followed by a few drops of rain.

It was just as hot at night, and if you slept in the open, you would be attacked by swarms of mosquitoes.

There was no air conditioning in those days, and we had to manage with a small table fan.

Every day the bhisti or water carrier would come around, splashing water from his goatskin bag on to the khus-khus matting that was draped

across our front door and windows. This had a delicious cooling effect.

Our drinking water was kept in an earthen jug or *sohrai*, which kept it fairly cool. We used water from the tap, as did everybody in the area; it was quite safe. Soda water was used by whisky drinkers, but my father did not touch alcohol.

For most of the day I was on my own.

'Why don't you play with those boys across the road?' asked my father, indicating another hutment occupied by a British family.

'I tried,' I said, 'but couldn't understand their language. Is it English?'

My father couldn't help laughing. 'Well, it's English, but they are cockneys from London. It sounds different from our English.'

It most certainly did!

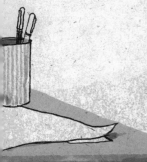

3

I was quite happy to be on my own while my father was away at work. I had a dartboard, a train set, lots of books and comics, and an old gramophone with a box of 78 rpm records. My father had a liking for grand opera, and anyone passing our hutment would have been startled by the voices of Caruso and Gigli belting out the great arias from *La Bohème* or *Madama Butterfly*. I enjoyed listening to these tenors and baritones, and the great Russian bass, Chaliapin.

My father would come home—usually by pony-driven tonga—at five or six in the evening, and after having tea together (lots of bread and jam for me), I would help him sort and arrange his postage stamps. He was an avid stamp collector, with separate albums for different countries. And the stamps would be arranged and mounted in sets; if a set was incomplete he would go to great lengths to complete it, even ordering stamps from Stanley Gibbons, the big stamp dealer in London.

There were illustrated Stanley Gibbons

catalogues lying around at home, and I would go through them every now and then, learning a good deal of stamp history in the process.

The stamps taught me quite a lot about history and geography, so that when I went to school again later I was far ahead of the other students in these subjects.

Delhi itself was full of history. One day my father took me to the Purana Kila, the rambling old fortress that had been the emperor Humayun's palace. We went up and down the steps of the ruined library—the steps down which Humayun had fallen to his untimely death. They did not appear to be very dangerous.

'Perhaps he was pushed,' I suggested.

'Well, strange things did happen in those days. There was always someone who wanted to be the king!'

And in our time it was Hitler who wanted to rule the world.

'No one rules the world forever,' said my father. 'The gods grow jealous. If someone is constantly successful or too powerful—be it Alexander or Napoleon or Hitler—the gods will eventually destroy him.'

'They don't like any competition, I suppose,' I added.

4

Well, in 1942 it didn't look as though Hitler would be beaten. And his ally, Japan, had overrun most of China, Malaysia, Singapore and Burma, and was poised for an invasion of India. Calcutta had been bombed on at least two occasions, and now air-raid shelters were coming up all over New Delhi.

Air-raid shelters? These were really long trenches dug up on the sides of important roads. If you jumped into one of them you were liable to break an ankle. But they were good fun for the street children. As soon as the monsoon broke, they filled up with rainwater, and naked urchins could be seen leaping in and out of them with shrieks of laughter.

It wasn't a lot of fun for us, unfortunately. The hutment was soon leaking all over the place, and we had to move.

My father rented two rooms in a bungalow on Atul Grove Lane, not far from Connaught Place, the commercial centre, and it was like moving from a shanty town to the environs of Buckingham Palace!

Atul Grove was a short lane leading off Curzon Road (new Kamala Nehru Marg). On one side of the lane was the telegraph department, fronted by a patch of lawn; on the other side, four or five

bungalows. An elderly couple in one of them gave us the tenancy of a portion of their house. My father and I shared the bedroom. The sitting room was almost entirely mine, crowded with a box full of books, the ever-present gramophone, a bagatelle board, dartboard, and so on. And there was a small dining room and kitchen. A part-time cook would drop in during the day to prepare our meals, but my father always made

the breakfast before leaving for office. First thing in the morning he would whip up the cream, for he preferred to make his own butter; then a couple of toasts for me, with a half-boiled egg (which I preferred to a full-boiled egg); occasionally a sausage; lots of jam; and lots of tea with condensed milk, the supply of fresh milk being erratic.

Yes, I was a greedy little boy.

*

The great thing about Atul Grove was that it was close to Connaught Place—to the cinemas, bookshops, record shops, restaurants. There were four cinema halls showing the latest Hollywood and British films, and whenever my father came home early he would take me to the pictures. That year I must have seen at least twenty films with him! Occasionally we dropped in at

Wenger's, the confectioners, and came home with patties and pastries. And I discovered the Milk Bar, then situated on the Outer Circle, only a short walk from Atul Grove. If I was feeling bored or lonely, I could walk down the road to the Milk Bar and treat myself to a chocolate or strawberry milkshake.

By now my father was a Flying Officer, which meant an additional stripe on his uniform. I loved putting on his RAF hat or cap, even though it was too large for me.

*

Sometimes we would drop in at Rankin's, the big draper's shop, where my father had his uniforms tailored. Mr Rankin, like my father, was an avid stamp collector, and Mr Rankin and Mr Bond would get together in a huddle, poring over their latest acquisition, sometimes making an exchange.

Stamps!

They were always there in the background, and very often in the foreground.

One evening I found a bottle of wine on the dining table.

'Daddy!' I exclaimed. 'Are we having wine with our dinner?'

'No, it's for a guest,' he explained. 'A young American officer is coming over to look at our stamp collection. He collects stamps from Greece, and I have some rare issues. I've asked him over for dinner. Most Americans drink wine, or something or the other.'

'Coca-Cola mostly.'

'That's only in films. It hasn't come to India as yet.'

This was the first time my father had invited anyone over for dinner, so it was quite an occasion.

Our guest arrived duly—a quiet, soft-spoken young man, quite unlike my notion of an American, which was based on characters portrayed on the screen by James Cagney or Wallace Beery—noisy fellows!

And our guest turned out to be a teetotaller—he wouldn't have any wine!

I was quite prepared to taste it, but my father hid the bottle in a cupboard, and I never saw it again. He may have given it to our landlord, who used to get a little tipsy every evening.

Anyway, the dinner was a success, the cook having excelled himself with a chocolate pudding. And dinner finished, Flying Officer Bond and Captain America sat down to look at stamps.

An hour passed, two hours, and I fell asleep on the sofa. When I woke up, Captain America was about to leave. He signed a cheque for Rs 2500 to Aubrey Bond, picked up a wallet full of stamps, which he had just bought, said goodbye and thanks for a lovely dinner, and disappeared into the night.

There was money in stamps, after all.

5

Who would have thought there was a war going on in Europe, Asia, North Africa and the Pacific? Who would have thought India would be an independent and sovereign nation in two or three years' time? There I was, enjoying chocolate milkshakes, while British and Indian civilians were trudging through the jungles of Burma to escape the Japanese advance.

My father was doing his duty, deciphering or helping to invent codes and

cyphers with which to circumvent the plans of
the enemy. He was too old for active service. After
the war, he told me we would leave for England.

'Why England, Daddy?' I asked. 'Their stamps
are so dull.'

'So where would you like to go?'

'Oh, Borneo or Zanzibar or the Canary
Islands. What lovely stamps they have!'

'You get head hunters in Borneo,' he said.
'Much safer just to collect their stamps.'

*

The rains were over, but it was hot and sticky and I was covered with prickly heat. It was impossible to escape the gnats and mosquitoes. My father fell ill with a severe attack of malaria. He had to be admitted to the military hospital, out at Palam. I was on my own.

For the first time in my life I was on my own.

On my own all day, on my own all night.

The landlord and his lady slept at the other end of the building. They were in their seventies and needed more help than I did. The cook came over every day at around noon and made my lunch and something extra for my dinner, but he

lived on the outskirts of Delhi, near Shahdara, and made his way home by bus every afternoon.

For two nights I was entirely on my own, sleeping on my father's bed, the window closed because the moths kept coming in, attracted by my reading light. A small clock ticked away on the mantelpiece.

The gecko lizards ticked away in their own fashion. Outside, on the road, a jackal howled. The street dogs responded, barking away through most of the night.

I read whatever I could find in the bookshelf—books that I hadn't ventured to read before: *Mr Midshipman Easy* by Captain Marryat, a rollicking adventure story which kept me company till dawn. The next night it was Stevenson's *Dr Jekyll and Mr Hyde*. This one scared me stiff, and I resolved to avoid horror stories, at least until my father returned.

I managed breakfast quite well, having learnt to whip up creamy butter, which I heaped up on my toast. I could boil an egg and brew a cup of tea. I pretended I was marooned on a desert island, surviving like a shipwrecked cabin boy, and this made it fun for a while. But towards evening I began to feel lonely. I missed my father. I missed his presence at the dining table, the talks

we had, the discussions about stamps, the visits to the cinema, the touch of his hand.

On the third evening I had company. Someone had arranged for a servant boy to come and sleep in the front room, in case of an emergency. And he turned out to be the son of the road sweeper who lived nearby. He was about my age, and I had often seen him cycling down the road, whistling cheerfully or singing snatches of some popular Hindi film song. He was usually barefooted, wearing shorts and an old sports shirt. He had grinned at me sometimes, his gleaming white teeth flashing in his dark face, but we hadn't spoken. He had a lovely chocolate complexion, which I rather envied, as I was too white on my body and too red on the face! Walking about in the fierce Delhi sun had given me a roasted look, so that our landlord called me

'Tandoori Ruskin' and the street boys called out 'Lal Bandar!' (Red Monkey) whenever I passed them.

My father had told me never to react, verbally or physically, to any abuse that I might encounter on the streets, and I took his advice, maintaining a stock silence if any comment was made about my looks or demeanour. 'And anyway,' he added, 'it's hardly an insult to be called a red monkey. There's a monkey god who is revered by all, and he's redder than you could ever hope to be!'

6

Raju, my bodyguard, turned up after dinner, made himself comfortable on the sofa and proceeded to entertain me with all the gossip of the mohalla. When this had been exhausted he told me tales of his village near Agra, including a scary one about a local raja who maintained a large pool full of crocodiles. Anyone who disobeyed him was thrown into the crocodile pool. As the crocodiles had to be fed regularly, many innocent people, boys and girls included, were flung into the pool to please the raja and his pets!

'That's why I'm here in Delhi,' said Raju. 'If I'd remained in my village I would have been thrown into the pool, sooner or later.'

'Breakfast for the crocodile,' I said. I did not believe his story, but later I learnt that there really *was* such a raja!

Captain Marryat and R.L. Stevenson took a back seat while Raju told me similar hair-raising stories, and it was past midnight before we both fell asleep on the sofa.

*

The next day Raju took me for a bicycle ride.

There was only the one bicycle, so of course I had to sit on the handlebar while he did all the work, pedalling furiously the whole time. The rains were over, sticky September had come and gone,

and we were slipping slowly
into that time of the year
when Delhi is at its
most congenial. We
rode all the way
to India Gate, and
up and down

all the roads in the capital area, and ate syrupy gulab jamuns at a stall in the Bengali market. Tired out by his exertions Raju fell asleep early that night, so I read a few pages of Captain Marryat, then fell asleep too.

*

On the following day the landlord and his wife invited me to have tea with them. There was bread and butter and strawberry jam. They were 'upper-caste' people and told me very gently that I should not be on the roads all day, roaming around with a 'low-caste' sweeper boy.

I remained quiet. I was a stubborn boy (and still very stubborn today) and when I wanted to do something I did not get into an argument; I just did what I wanted to do. I finished all their bread and jam, said thank you very politely and went back to playing with Raju.

There were, of course, other boys to play with, and sometimes I would join them in kicking a football around on the open ground in front of the telegraph offices.

One of these was Joseph, a friendly boy from Travancore, in the south, whose father was a senior clerk in the department.

'Which school do you go to?' he asked me.

'I've finished school,' I said airily. 'I have a job, I work for my father!'

Raju had a job too, but out of sheer necessity, and so he could not go to school. But he could ride a cycle faster than anyone, and he could tell amazing stories—like the one about a jungle boy who protected the wild animals from hunters, leading the hunters into a bog, where they were all sucked down into the mud with only their topis left floating on the surface! Raju was my hero, no doubt about it!

*

After nearly a fortnight my father came home from the hospital, looking very weak and tired. But he resumed his duties with codes and cyphers, and I resumed mine, sorting his stamps. Raju returned to his quarters, but I continued to see him whenever he was free from his own arduous duties as a cleaner and errand boy in the telegraph offices.

As winter set in, my father's health improved, and we began visiting the bookshops and cinemas again. He took me to see the Red Fort in Old Delhi, and we wandered about the palaces and pavilions.

From its ramparts we had a good view of the Yamuna as it wended its way across the countryside, towards sacred Mathura and historic Agra. On the archway of one of the pavilions there was a line in Persian which, translated by my father, went, 'If there be a heaven on earth, it is this, it is this, it is this!'

The poet who had written that must have been a happy man, I thought. It was very windy on the ramparts of the fort, and a lot of blood had been shed within its confines, so it was not exactly my idea of heaven (I would have preferred eating cakes at Wenger's), but the view across the river was quite spectacular, and I suppose it was that which had inspired the poet.

We thought of dropping in on Uncle Fred, but there was a disturbance at the railway station, so we decided to move on. The Quit India Movement was still at its height. There were no cell phones then, and getting in touch with Uncle Fred would have meant making our way through an excited crowd. My father, in his uniform, might have been mistaken for a police officer.

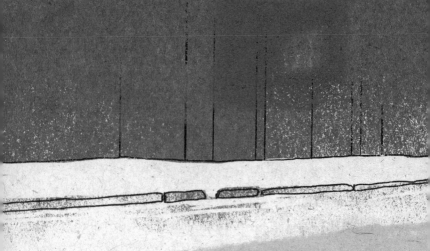

And policemen were not very popular at the time.

We took a tonga to Maiden's Hotel, which was in a quiet corner of Old Delhi, and had our lunch on a sunny verandah. Maiden's was a very beautiful building, surrounded by lawns and a variety of trees.

'Why is it called Maiden's?' I asked.

'It was built and run by a man called John Maiden,' said my father. 'Not many people know that.'

And then he came around to the subject of my schooling.

'There's a fine old school in Simla,' he told me. 'I think you'll like it there, Ruskin.'

'But, Daddy, I want to stay with you!'

'I may be transferred soon. To Karachi or Calcutta, or possibly even to Ceylon. I won't be allowed to take you with me.'

'Who'll sort your stamps? Who'll go to the pictures with you?'

'There'll be plenty of time for that during your holidays. And this war won't last forever. Hitler is on the run from the Russians, and the Japanese are being pushed back. Another year or two and it will be over.'

He was right in his predictions about the war, but meanwhile I had to go to a boarding school again. I had enjoyed a year's holiday. Would I be able to catch up with the other children, or would I be the dunce of my class? And would my new school be as awful as the last one?

7

And so, a couple of months later, I was sitting beside my father in the railcar that took the winding, narrow-gauge railway track up the hills to Simla. The journey by the railcar took about four hours as compared to the eight taken by the tiny mountain train, pulled up steep inclines by a small but sturdy steam engine, huffing and puffing as it sent plumes of coal smoke trailing behind it. We overtook it at Barog, a pretty little station about halfway to Simla, where we stopped for breakfast. The Barog breakfast was famous in its day—superior to railway breakfasts elsewhere. And the Barog tunnel must have been one of the longest in the world. It took us all of five minutes to pass through it.

Although we were already a few weeks late, my father very wisely did not take me straight

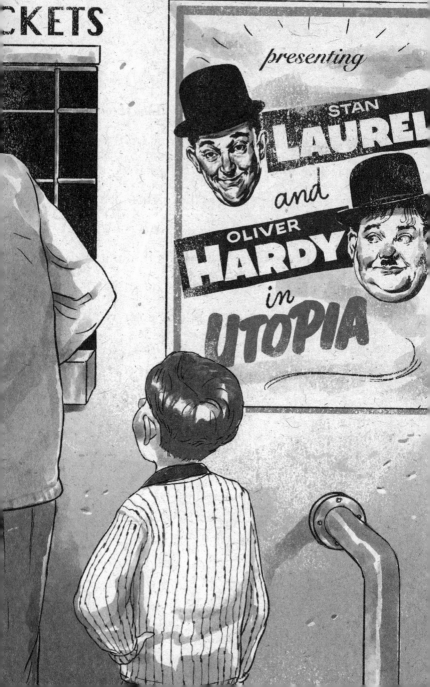

to my intended school, but gave me a three-day holiday in Simla, spending all his time with me.

We went to the pictures, of course. Laurel and Hardy always cheered me up. And we went to Dario's, the famous restaurant on Mall. And up the hill to the Jako temple, where the monkeys snatched away all our pastries.

And then a long rickshaw ride around Elysium Hill, the two of us in a single rickshaw, while I listened to my father recounting Kipling's story of 'The Phantom Rickshaw'. I would read it for myself a year or two later.

And then, inevitably, there was the rickshaw ride down to Chhota Simla, where my school—the prep school, not the senior school—was situated.

Standing on the path above the small playground, I got my first sight of my future companions—a noisy mob of some two hundred children, milling about on the field, engaged in a variety of activities. Some were kicking a ball around. Some were playing hop sets. One boy had a butterfly net and was chasing a bright blue butterfly. Some were rolling about in the dust, wrestling with each other. One was blowing a tin trumpet. Another was beating a drum. No one seemed to be in charge.

I really did not feel like joining that lot!

'Isn't there another school I can go to, Daddy?'

But it was too late to change schools.

From the building behind us came the strains of a violin. We stepped up to the window and looked in. A florid-faced gentleman was

making strange noises on a violin, while a long-faced woman accompanied him on the piano.

'That's your headmaster and his wife,' said my father. 'He plays well, doesn't he?'

'I don't think so,' I said, always forthright in my opinions. 'It's too squeaky.'

8

I did not cry or make a fuss when my dad said goodbye. He had promised to come up and see me at the first opportunity, and I knew he would keep his word. Having spent many days on my own in the Atul Grove flat, I had developed a certain fortitude, an ability to stand alone, a dependence on myself rather than on others. I was devoted to only one person—my father. And when he wasn't around, I got on with what I wanted to do.

It took me some time to make new friends among my fellows; but they were on the whole an easy-going lot, and the general atmosphere was certainly less oppressive than that of the convent school where I had first been a prisoner. The fact that the boys could make such a tremendous noise while the headmaster concentrated on playing his violin meant that the school was a little different from others.

To my surprise, I had no difficulty in competing with the rest of my class. I was well ahead of the others in history, geography, general knowledge and essay writing. That year with my father and his stamps hadn't gone to waste. I was the only boy who knew where the Solomon Islands were situated. And that Iraq had a boy king. And that polar bears never ate penguins because they lived on opposite Poles. I was given a promotion, right at the start of the school year.

A long letter came from my father—the first of many. He wrote about his plans for the future—of leaving India when the war was over, and of finding a good school for me in England.

And colourful postcards arrived regularly—postcards depicting famous trains or ocean liners; butterflies of the world; exotic birds and animals; famous cricketers and football players. The postcard collection was soon the envy of the other boys.

The headmaster was a bit strange, playing his violin at odd times, but the teachers were a decent lot, and the boys were friendly.

School wasn't so bad, after all.

THE SCHOOL IN THE HILLS

1

'Paddle your own canoe,' my father had said, and I was determined to do just that.

Back in the strict convent school in Mussoorie, I had been shy, reserved, unwilling to make friends. But the year in New Delhi with my father had given me a feeling of independence and confidence. When he was

in hospital I had managed quite well on my own. I had made friends with the boys across the road. And in my father's company, talking about the war and the future of India and the lives of people in other countries, I had become more knowledgeable and worldly-wise than most children of my age.

The school in which I now found myself was fairly strict, but it was only the prep school and not as harsh or rigid as the senior school, which I would join two years later.

The staff and teachers were an odd assortment. We had a headmaster who did not teach but who, as I mentioned earlier, played the violin at odd times of the day or night. His wife did not teach either, but spent a good deal of her time prowling about the corridors and dormitories trying to catch us out in various misdemeanours, such as pillow fighting, wrestling on the beds or singing loudly. Punishment, however, was not too severe. A whack or two on our backsides with the flat of a hairbrush was the worst we could expect.

We had heard of the horrors of being caned in senior school, but senior school was out of sight (quite literally being situated on another spur of the mountain) and nothing to do with us, except when we were herded there once a month to attend a Sunday chapel service or a school play.

The headmaster and his wife were called Mr and Mrs Priestley. Apart from playing the violin and the piano, the Priestleys grew rhubarb, a sickly sweet vegetable, on a patch of ground behind their cottage, and as a result we were given rhubarb pudding at least twice a week at lunchtime. By the end of summer everyone hated rhubarb.

There were three or four young teachers— Miss Das, Mr Young, Mr Murtough, Miss D'Cruz (who ate peanuts in class)—and an older, senior teacher, Mr Oliver, a bachelor who lived with his pet dachshund, an unfriendly dog who occasionally bit people. Mr Oliver had a name for the dog, but everyone else called it Hitler.

Mr Oliver was a lonely man, reserved and taciturn. The story went that he had been jilted by the girl he loved, but this may only have been a story. He did not look the romantic type. The romantic type was Mr Young, a dashing bronze Indian who had pictures of popular American movie stars (such as Betty Grable and Alice Faye) tacked up on the walls of his study. Betty Grable was famous for her long legs while Alice Faye sang sultry love songs to soldiers serving in various war zones.

Mr Murtough was the games master, Miss Das took junior classes, and Miss D'Cruz taught geography and music (to those who were interested) and conducted the school choir.

Miss D'Cruz soon discovered that I couldn't sing a high note. I was strictly a low-note person.

But she wanted me in the choir because, as she said, I looked 'cute' in a cassock and surplice.

'Now listen, Bond,' she ordered, 'I want you to open your mouth with the others, to look as though you are singing, but you are not to allow any sound to issue from your vocal cords. Not a note, high or low, do you follow me?'

'Yes, ma'am.'

'Good. So let's proceed with this sweet lullaby.'

I followed her instructions during rehearsals; but at the final performance, held in the senior school chapel, I could not resist letting out a booming low note, in the manner of the great Russian bass Chaliapin. The audience did not appear to mind, but Miss D'Cruz went into a frenzy and did not speak to me for weeks.

'That awful boy, Bond,' she was heard saying to the headmaster, 'he did his best to ruin our choir festival!'

2

'That awful boy, Bond' sank deeper into Miss D'Cruz's bad books by letting in a goal while substituting as a goalkeeper in the junior hockey team. The match was against a rival school, considered our inferiors; but they were our superiors at hockey.

While we were still on the field a message was delivered to me by one of the boys.

'Miss D'Cruz says to tell you that you are as clumsy as a doodwalla.'

Why this prejudice against milkmen? They were not the ones who spilt the milk. Anyway, I told the messenger to go back and tell her that she was a doodwalli, a milkmaid. She must have been flattered because, instead of giving me the back end of her hairbrush, she started giving me coy looks and even offered me the occasional

peanut. Perhaps Mr Young, with whom she had been friendly, had fallen out of favour with her.

*

I made at least three good friends that year. One was Bimal Mirchandani, a Bombay boy, also known as 'Bambi' because he was very slender and slim, just like the young gazelle in the Disney film of that name. Another was Napinder— 'Nappy'—a Sikh boy from the Punjab. He and his younger brother Joginder were the only Sikh boys in the school at that time. Both were very good-natured.

And then there was Riaz, a friendly Pathan from Peshawar, who became a close friend only after we had come to blows.

I don't remember what the fight was about—obviously something trivial—but I remember us pummelling each other with our fists, much to the delight of a small crowd of onlookers. In the process he knocked out one of my teeth, but he was the worse for this because my tooth had become embedded in his hand and could only be extracted with some difficulty.

The fight was declared a draw.

3

Mr Oliver, a Scoutmaster in his youth, decided to take up scouting again one day, and set about forming a troop of Boy Scouts, enlisting those who were good at tying knots, or identifying certain stars and planets in the night sky, or climbing the rope which he suspended from the upper flat to the rhubarb patch.

I wasn't good at any of those things. If I tied a knot, I couldn't open it. I could identify the Milky Way (or pretended to), but the other constellations were just stars to me.

'You'll never be an astronomer,' said Mr Oliver gloomily.

'No, sir,' I replied, 'but an astrologer, maybe?'

'Off with you! And try climbing that rope.'

But halfway up the rope I gave up and fell into the rhubarb patch.

'Is there anything you can do well, Bond?' asked Mr Oliver.

'I can boil an egg, sir.'

So he gave me a Cookery badge.

*

Twelve of us were taken on an outing to Tara Devi, where there was a Boy Scouts jamboree—a get-together of Scouts from different schools. We were taught how to set up tents, and there were four of us to a tent. We were also taught how to make small fires with twigs and dry leaves.

'Not so many leaves, Bond,' said Mr Oliver, 'you don't want to start a forest fire.'

With the help of Bimal and Riaz I managed to light a fire, on the top of which we placed a huge *degchi* containing a generous amount of cooking fat. Into this went all the vegetables I could lay my hands on—potatoes, tomatoes, turnips, chunks of cabbage and cauliflower, green chillies, red chillies, fat chillies, slim chillies.

When everything was cooking nicely, each of us took a spoonful to see if we'd got the flavour right.

'Too hot,' said Bimal.

'Too dull,' said Riaz.

'We must liven it up,' I said, and opened a tin of strawberry jam. I emptied the contents into the simmering pot.

Everyone had a taste.

'Super,' said Bimal.

'Terrific,' said Riaz. 'We'll call it an all-India stew.'

'Or a Bond bhujia,' said Nappy.

Everyone tucked in, and by midnight everyone (including Mr Oliver) was groaning with indigestion. We returned to school a day earlier than planned.

'Never mind,' said Mr Oliver, patting me on the back. 'It was a noble effort.' And he allowed me to keep my Cookery badge.

4

Food plays an important part in the life of a boarding-school boy. The daily fare, no matter how nutritious, palls after some time. The school tuck shop provided samosas (edible only when hot and fresh) and packets of peanut toffee (*gur-patti*), but not much else. We were allowed into town once a month to spend our pocket money (five rupees), and mine usually went into

buying comic papers such as *Film Fun* or *The Dandy*. There were also story papers such as *The Champion* and *The Hotspur*, which were popular during the war years.

But the big event was getting a parcel from home. These parcels generally contained delicacies such as chocolates or tins of jam or pickle, and the recipients would usually share the contents with his close friends. Those who did not share their food parcels were given a rough time.

When a parcel was opened, friends and familiars would gather around in feverish anticipation. A cheer would go up if chocolates or chewing gum or toffees made an appearance. But there would be groans of disappointment if the parcel happened to contain useful items such as socks or handkerchiefs or underwear.

My father was not a great one for making up parcels, preferring to send me picture postcards of famous ocean liners, trains, birds, racehorses, or famous fictional characters such as Mr Pickwick or Long John Silver or the Mad Hatter, with little messages on the reverse suggesting that I read the books in which these characters appeared—that is, *Pickwick Papers*, *Treasure Island*, *Alice in Wonderland*, and others. (And in due course I did read all of them!)

But, as I said, food did play an important part in our lives, and when a friend of my father's came by one day and handed me a carton full of tinned foods—Kraft cheese, condensed milk, rock candy from Calcutta and guava cheese from Allahabad—the number of my friends increased dramatically! It's like that in the greater world too, isn't it? Give a party, and your friends double.

Riaz and I rescued a tin of Kraft cheese after the free-for-all, and found a quiet spot on the hillside, in the shade of an old plum tree. Processed cheese was hard to obtain during wartime, and we did not waste any of it; we simply worked our way through all the blocks, leaving nothing for the rest of the gang.

We then used our penknives to carve our names in the trunk of the tree. This bid for immortality was common enough among most of us. 'We too were here,' was what we were trying to say. 'We too had our special moment upon Planet Earth.'

But the plum tree must have gone by now. It was an old tree even then.

*

We were inclined to take nature for granted in those days. We had our forests and lakes and unpolluted rivers. There were still many birds and animals to be seen. Wild flowers covered the hill slopes. Crickets sang in the grass.

There was a small stream at the bottom of the hill, and sometimes we broke bounds in order to visit it and paddle in its shallow, clear waters. If we were caught we were given the back of Mr Priestley's large hairbrush, but we didn't mind; the escapade was worth the punishment.

On one occasion, Bambi came back with a bucket full of tadpoles, which he introduced into the little pond that fronted Mr Priestley's home

and office. By the end of the monsoon it was overflowing with frogs.

There were frogs everywhere—in the dormitory, in the classrooms, in the dining hall, on the playing field . . . Miss D'Cruz organized a great frog hunt, and all the boys went about with sticks and buckets, collecting frogs, and letting them loose further down the road. Many of them found their way into the grounds of the governor's house. Their croaking kept the governor awake at night. So he told his aide-de-camp to get rid of them. The ADC phoned the municipality, who, not having frog-catchers, sent over a team of dogcatchers. The dogcatchers said it wasn't their job to catch frogs and went away sulking. 'Phone the fire brigade,' ordered the governor. The ADC phoned the fire brigade and they arrived with their hoses and swept all the frogs away by flooding the grounds.

5

My father came to see me towards the end of August.

'Someone to see you,' said Mr Young. 'In the office verandah. A surprise visitor.'

'It's my Daddy!' I shouted, recognizing him from the far end of the playground. I ran across the field and flung myself into his waiting arms.

'You look well, Ruskin,' he said. 'School seems to agree with you.'

'Home is better,' I said. 'And there are only three months left for the holidays. Will we still be living in Delhi?'

'I've been transferred to Calcutta. You'll like it there too. There are bookshops and cinemas and a big maidan. And ships come up the river from Rangoon and Java and Hong Kong.'

He was in Simla just for a day, and he took me out for a rickshaw ride, but it was raining the entire time, so we settled down in Dario's, which was fine by me, as the menu was long and interesting.

Over a shammi kabab I said, 'I'm scared of ships, ever since that Arab dhow nearly sank.' I was referring to a short voyage we had made across the Gulf of Kutch, when I was very small. That was before the war, when my father had been working for the Jamnagar ruler.

'These are mostly steamships,' said my father. 'And maybe we'll go to England in one of them. The war should be over soon.'

'Do we have to go to England?'

'Well, India will soon be free and we may have to go. And those of us who joined the RAF will be demobbed—out of a job! We'll have to make a living somewhere.'

I thought of that for a moment, then thought of a brilliant solution.

'We could sell stamps!' I was referring to his superb stamp collection, of course.

'We could indeed,' he said. 'And I've already sold a few rare items, to pay for the passage.'

'We could open a stamp shop,' I said enthusiastically. 'But we won't sell all of them—not those beautiful Cayman Island stamps!'

'They will all be yours, Ruskin.'

We make our plans, but Life plays tricks on all of us. It has an agenda of its own. That stamp collection was never to be mine.

In spite of the mist and the rain, it was a wonderful day—a day that I would never forget. It was to be the last time I saw my father—but, of course, I did not know that at the time.

*

Back in school with my friends, we too made our plans—plans for the holidays, plans for the next term, plans for the time when we would be grown-up. We had our dreams. And it's fine to dream, provided we can deal with the reality when we wake up. We dream, we plan, and sometimes the plans come off. And if they don't, we must plan again.

6

The rain clouds receded, and a golden glow spread over the mountains as autumn came to the Simla hills. On the slope above the playground the mauve- and-white petals of the cosmos spread out like a colourful quilt, while the headmaster's garden was a profusion of flowering chrysanthemums, dahlias and giant marigolds. Mr Priestley was inspired to greater efforts on his violin, and Mrs Priestley tossed her head and attacked the

piano keys as though she would extract every last chord from them. It was an ancient piano, and although someone from Delhi or Lahore came to tune it once a year, it remained obstinately tuneless. Wooden-faced Priestley calmly plied the bow of his violin; an agitated spouse dripped perspiration as she struggled to extract a little music from that lifeless piano.

It transpired that a colony of mice were living within it, nibbling at the wires, but even when they had been removed, the piano refused to respond. Under Miss D'Cruz's direction the choir sang obediently, with or without piano accompaniment. She played gramophone

RESIGNATION LETT

ster of ca

records in the background, and we dutifully sang in unison with them. Or rather, the choir sang; I was still under a stricture of silence.

Mr Young got engaged to Miss D'Cruz, the marriage to take place during the winter holidays. Mr Murtough had a row with the headmaster and put in his resignation. Mr Oliver lost his dog.

It happened one evening while he was taking Hitler for a walk in the forest. It wasn't really a forest, just a clump of pine trees on the ridge above the school. A leopard sprang out of the bushes and made off with the dachshund, leaving poor Mr Oliver holding a broken lead. A brief yelp, and Hitler was gone, providing a light supper for a hungry leopard.

Mr Oliver went into mourning and did not speak to anyone for days. So Mr Young organized a subscription, and we all contributed eight annas each out of our pocket money, until we had collected almost two hundred rupees, which was enough to buy a little terrier pup from a lady who bred dogs, and this we presented to Mr Oliver. He was very pleased and thanked us all in a moving little speech during the morning assembly, but although he took good care of the little terrier, we could tell it wasn't the same; he really missed his old companion.

The war was coming to an end. In Europe, the real Hitler was suffering one defeat after another, and in Asia, the invading Japanese were being pushed back. The aggressors had overreached themselves and run out of steam.

*

The rains were over, and our annual 'marathon' was held. It extended from the governor's house to the school gate, barely a couple of miles, and we did not overexert ourselves although, Mr Young and Miss D'Cruz would be stationed at strategic

points to cheer us on and to see that we did not wander off into the Chhota Simla bazar.

I had come in somewhere at the end of the struggling line of runners, when one of the boys who was not in the race came up to me and said Mr Young wanted to see me urgently.

Poor Mr Young. He'd been handed the unenviable task of giving me bad news. Not just bad news. The worst possible news. Life-shattering news.

This was something the headmaster should have done. But Mr Priestley was busy practising on his violin, and his wife did not think it was her duty.

Mr Young did his best. He put his hand on my shoulder and led me down past the school gate, down an avenue of young deodars.

'Your dear father,' he stammered. 'Your dear father—God needed him for other things—'

I knew what was coming, and I burst into tears. I had no one else in the world—just that one dear father—and he had been snatched away. We had been taught that God was a loving, merciful being, and here he was doing the cruelest possible thing to a small boy. Why did he need my father? What could he possibly want him for? Did he want his stamp collection?

That stamp collection would disappear during the following months. A relative, not God, would get hold of it, sell the lot and keep the proceeds. But I wasn't thinking of that just then. I only knew that I was alone in the world thereon.

Mr Young led me down to the school infirmary and handed me over to the nursing matron.

'The Head says to keep him here for a couple of days until he feels better. I'll send some of his things down.'

I was the only person in that little ward. I don't think it helped to be left on my own. All I could do was brood. Think about the past and brood over the future.

Remember all the days I'd spent with my father during that year and a half in Delhi: helping him with his wonderful stamp collection; going to the pictures with him, to the bookshops and cafés in Connaught Place; holding his hand as he led me through the portals of old monuments—tombs and forts and palaces—and told me the stories that were buried beneath those ruins. And even when I'd been on my own—when he was away all day on duty, or ill in hospital—I had always known he would soon be home, walking in at the front door, tired but smiling, always smiling . . .

I would feel his presence in the years to come, and that presence would protect and sustain me. But just then, in that cold and empty hospital ward, I felt friendless, abandoned.

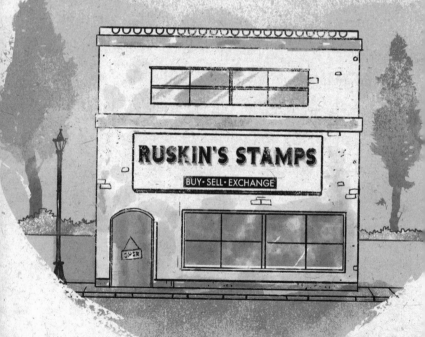

Two days later, when I returned to the dormitory, I found my father's letters and postcards and read them again and again. Mr Priestley found me poring over those letters and suggested that he keep them for me. He probably thought it was an unhealthy thing for a small boy to be constantly going over his father's words. I gave him the letters, but held one back, his last letter, the one I still have with me today, over seventy year later. I still read it from time to time. Mr Priestley can't stop me now!

He probably meant well, but at the end of the year, when I went to his office and asked for the letters, he acted as though he had no memory of them.

'What letters?' he stammered. 'Did you give me your letters? I don't remember, boy. You must be mistaken.' He made a show of going through his desk drawers, coming up with nothing. 'I don't have any letters. Concentrate on your studies, my boy. You're going home to your mother. Perhaps you'll return next year. Off with you now—enjoy your holidays!'

I retired to the dormitory empty-handed, and Mr Priestley returned to his violin.

I was going home to my mother and to a stepfather I did not know. The future looked bleak.

My friends were very good to me, especially Riaz, who told me that even if I did not return to school he would keep in touch with me, and that I would at least receive *his* letters.

We went for a long walk through the pines and made plans for the future. Boyhood plans are wonderful things. They seldom materialize—time and circumstance spoil the best of plans—but it's good to make them, and to keep making them, for where there is a plan there is a hope, and, who knows, sometime a plan, a dream, might come to fruition.

Come November, and the small mountain train was full of small boys making a great deal of noise. It was holiday time and they were all going home. Goodbye, school! Goodbye, rhubarb pie! Goodbye, Mr Priestley and your violin! Goodbye, Simla!

Slowly, the little engine huffed and puffed, taking its contingent of small boys down to Kalka, where they would disperse, taking trains to distant parts of the great subcontinent.

They were going home, and although I had no idea what my new home would be like, or whether I would return to boarding school, I joined in the singing.

'Bye-bye rainy day, bye-bye snow,

We are on our way—here we go!

Rolling round the world, looking for the rainbow

We know we're going to find some day!'

Acknowledgements

The author wishes to thank Hemali Sodhi and the Puffin team for bringing out this little book in time for my eighty-third birthday. As I gave them the story at the last moment, they had to work swiftly on the text and illustrations. My special thanks go to Sohini Mitra, Nimmy Chacko and Ahlawat Gunjan for their efforts and enthusiasm, and to Mihir Joglekar for his evocative illustrations, all done at short notice. I am a lucky writer, being in the hands of such a fine editorial team.

Read More by Ruskin Bond

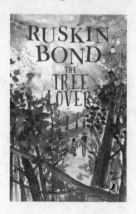

The Tree Lover

Everything that you've always loved about
Ruskin Bond is back.

His mesmerizing descriptions of nature and
his wonderful way with words—this is
Ruskin Bond at his finest.

Read on as Rusty tells the story of his grandfather's
relationship with the trees around him, and how he
is convinced that they love him back with as much
tenderness as he showers on them.

This beautifully illustrated edition brings to life one of
Bond's most enduring tales and is sure to win over yet
another generation of readers.

The Day Grandfather
Tickled a Tiger

A heart-warming story of love and friendship

When Grandfather discovers a little tiger cub on
a hunting expedition, he decides to take it home.
Christened Timothy, the cub grows up as any regular
house pet, with a monkey and a mongrel for company.
But as he grows older, Timothy starts behaving strangely,
and Grandfather decides that it's time to send him away.

This sumptuously illustrated edition brings to life one of
Bond's most captivating stories.

Cricket for the Crocodile

'Nakoo got his teeth deep into the cricket ball and
chewed. Revenge was sweet.'

Ranji's team finds an unexpected opponent—a nosy
crocodile—when it plays a cricket match against the
village boys. Annoyed at the swarm of boys crowding the
riverbank and the alarming cricket balls plopping around
his place of rest, Nakoo the crocodile decides to take his
revenge.

This sumptuously illustrated edition brings alive yet
another one of Ruskin Bond's delightful tales.

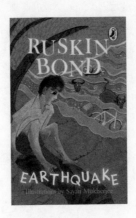

Earthquake

'What do you do when there's an earthquake?'
asked Rakesh.

Everyone in the Burman household has different ideas,
but nobody is prepared when the ground starts to shake
and quake, to crack and crumble, and half the town,
including their own house, comes down like a
pack of cards . . .

Can Rakesh and his family survive one of the worst
disasters to hit Shillong?

This stunningly illustrated edition breathes new life into
one of Ruskin Bond's most hair-raising tales.

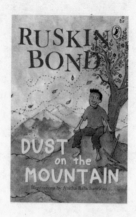

Dust on the Mountain

'The hill station, with all its glitter, was just a pretty gift box with nothing inside.'

When twelve-year-old Bisnu decides to go to Mussorie to earn for his family, he has no idea how dangerous and lonely life in a town can be for a boy on his own.

As he sets out to work on the limestone quarries, with the choking dust enveloping the beautiful mountain air, he finds that he longs for his little village in the Himalayas.

Anitha Balachandran's illustrations add a bright splash of colour to one of Ruskin Bond's most memorable stories.